BEWARE!

**Mortimer's madcap
plans and crazy ideas
could rub off on you!**

First published in 2014 by Hodder Children's Books

Text copyright © Tim Healey 2014
Illustrations copyright © Chris Mould 2014

Hodder Children's Books, 338 Euston Road, London, NW1 3BH
Hodder Children's Books Australia, Level 17/207 Kent Street, Sydney, NSW 2000

A catalogue record of this book is available from the British Library.

ISBN 978 0 340 99775 8

Printed in China

Hodder Children's Books is a division of Hachette Children's Books,
an Hachette UK Company

www.hachette.co.uk

MORTIMER KeeNe

ALIEN ABDUCTION

Tim Healey and Chris Mould

SAINT BARNABAS
SB
SCHOOL

Mortimer Keene

Age: 8
Special features: specs
Weak point: none!
Favourite phrase:
'By golly, I'm good!'

SAINT BARNABAS
SB
SCHOOL

Oliver Morris

Age: 9
Special features:
loves his food
Weak point: weak stomach
Favourite phrase:
'Oh no, not again.'

SAINT BARNABAS SCHOOL

S B

Jeremy Harrison

Age: 8
Special features:
carries a catapult
Weak point: short-sighted
Favourite phrase:
'Drat! Missed!'

SAINT BARNABAS SCHOOL

S B

Emily Bruce

Age: 8
Special features:
plays the cello
Weak point:
prefers to play marbles
Favourite phrase:
'Bombsies!'

SAINT BARNABAS SCHOOL

Year Seven

Age: 11–12 year olds
Special features: yawn a lot
Weak point:
don't get Shakespeare
Favourite phrase:
'It's like, hullo?'

SAINT BARNABAS SCHOOL

Kate Moore

Age: 8
Special features: pigtails
Weak point:
nervous disposition
Favourite phrase: 'Aargh!'

SAINT BARNABAS

S
B

SCHOOL

The Colonel

Age: 49
Special features:
very loud voice
Weak point: never listens
Favourite phrase: 'Zap it!'

It was quiet that day
At St. Barnabas School.
Summer was over,
The weather quite cool,

When a mothership landed!
Mr Field gave a shout
As from its dark portals
Strange Beings streamed out.

'Extraterrestrials!

Children, beware!'
Then he flopped in a faint
Back into his chair.

Oliver Morris
Was doing a poo
When a squat little being
Walked into the loo!

Oliver shrieked
And ran from the place
With his pants round his knees
And fear on his face.

HOWLING broke out
By the bicycle shed
Where a very tall being
Poked round its head.

'Just what are you after?'
Cried Mrs Moray.
'If we cannot help you

Then please go away!'

She called to her pupils,
Did Mrs Moray,
Appealing for calm:
'I've something to say!

We've been here before,
You know what I mean?
This may be the doing
Of Mortimer Keene.'

Keene was a genius,
Quiet and cool,
Friendly and normal,
Brilliant at school.

Though sometimes alarming,
As well as amazing,
When gripped by a project
With all systems blazing.

They found the boy quickly
But that was no use;
He was just playing marbles
With Emily Bruce.

And worse was to come
As from Year Seven
There came a grim cry:

'They've got Mr Bevan!'

With horrified groans
All watched with dismay
As young Mr Bevan
Was wafted away.

The Mothership waited,
Its portals gaped wide
And poor Mr Bevan
Was taken inside.

Then Jeremy Harrison
Gasped, 'This is daft!
The Beings are now going
Back to their craft!'

The aliens were off!
All watched goggle-eyed
As they got to their spaceship
And vanished inside.

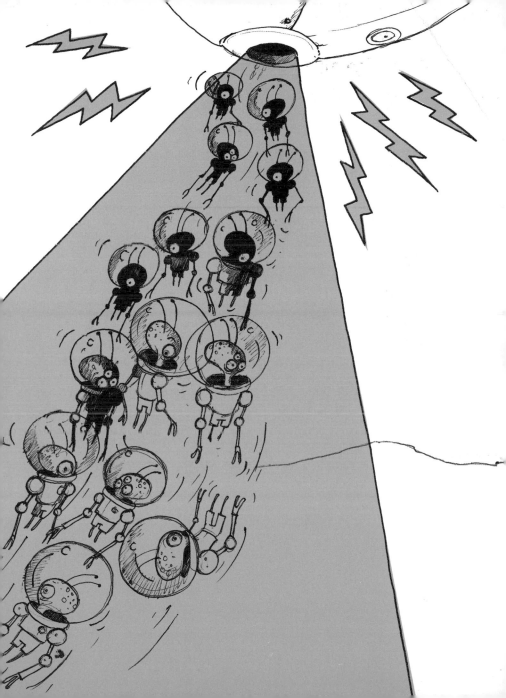

Mr Green wrung his hands
And gave out a yelp:
'Mortimer, lad, please
Do something to help!'

Mortimer frowned:
'I've been having some fun
Constructing a new kind of
Gravity Gun.'

'We could, I suppose,
Make a gravity shield
Around our own
Zero-point energy field…

Though I've got to ask why
You imagine the worst?
We should certainly try
To make contact first.'

Then the Army arrived;
They had seen the craft land.
All sighed with relief
Now that help was at hand.

'We may have to blast it,'
The Colonel declared.
'It'll make a loud bang,
So please don't be scared.'

RECEPTION

'I forbid you to blast it!'
Cried Mrs Moray.
'Mr Bevan's inside!
Just hold fire, I say.'

But the Colonel heard nothing;

He gave out a shout:

'Zap it!' he barked.

And a missile zoomed out.

Wailing was heard as
The kids in Year Seven
Imagined the fate
Of poor Mr Bevan.

But just as the missile
Started to fly
The alien spacecraft
Rose high in the sky!

The missile sped on
And the outcome was grim:
It flashed through the air
And hit the school gym!

'You blithering man!'
Cried Mrs Moray.
'Just look at my gym!
You've blown it away!'

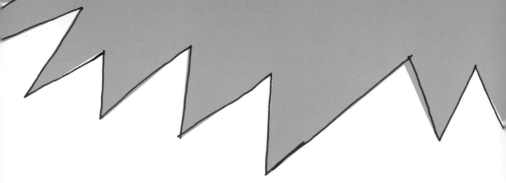

Teachers and pupils
Gathered around
As the Mothership gently
Returned to the ground.

'Don't fire again,
Don't fire, I say!
You'll blow us all up!'
Cried Mrs Moray.

'Please fetch me my laptop
At once, Mr Green.
We must now make contact,'
Said Mortimer Keene.

Mr Green brought the laptop
And Mortimer tapped
Something into the keyboard,
Then hooted and clapped.

'By golly I'm good,'
He cried out in glee.
'I'm inside their spacecraft:
Come quickly and see!'

All clustered around
Young Mortimer Keene,
Some hardly daring
To look at his screen:

Poor Mr Bevan,
Was he in pain?
Were aliens stealing
His thoughts from his brain?

Inside the Mothership
Young Mr Bevan
Thought he had died
And gone straight to heaven.

He lay on a couch
And was far from in pain;
He was eating smoked salmon
And sipping champagne.

Two slender beings
Brought treat after treat
While others, adoringly,
Sat at his feet.

He told them of *Shakespeare*
And when he spoke
They paid rapt attention
And laughed at each joke.

'We'll soon get you out,'
Cried Mrs Moray.
'Somehow we'll do it,
We will find a way.'

'I don't want to come out!'
Said young Mr Bevan.
'I'm fed up with school
And the kids in Year Seven.

These aliens are great;
They're marvellous blokes.
I'm teaching them *Shakespeare*,
They laugh at my jokes.'

Everyone watching
Was slightly unnerved.
'He must have gone crazy,'
The Colonel observed.

Mortimer answered:
'You're the one that is mad.
Strange beings are not
Necessarily bad.'

He tapped at his laptop
Incredibly fast:
'You'll never believe it!
I'VE MADE CONTACT AT LAST!'

He got a response
And read it with ease,
Then walked to the spacecraft
As bold as you please.

A Menacing Being Appeared on the scene.

'Delighted to meet you,'
Said Mortimer Keene.

'Come, Mr Bevan,
Close up your tome.
They have learnt enough now
And it's time to go home.'

With a sigh of regret
Mr Bevan complied.
The spacecraft doors opened,
They were soon back outside.

'They needed a teacher,
That was their quest:
A teacher of *Shakespeare.*
They said I'm the best!'

One of the aliens
Waved fondly goodbye.
Then the Mothership rose
Straight up into the sky.

School got back to normal
– The gym needed repair –
And that was the end
Of the whole strange affair.

But a change now came over
The kids in Year Seven,
Who paid rapt attention
To young Mr Bevan.

And Mortimer Keene?
All now sought his views
On luminous beings;
He went on the news.

'On meeting an alien
Find someone who knows
How to make contact;
Don't come straight to blows.'

'They could have turned nasty?'
Enquired the news team.

'All's well that ends well,'
Smiled Mortimer Keene.

Following these events
Mortimer Keene became
a national celebrity and was
often consulted by the
Government on issues relating
to extraterrestrials.

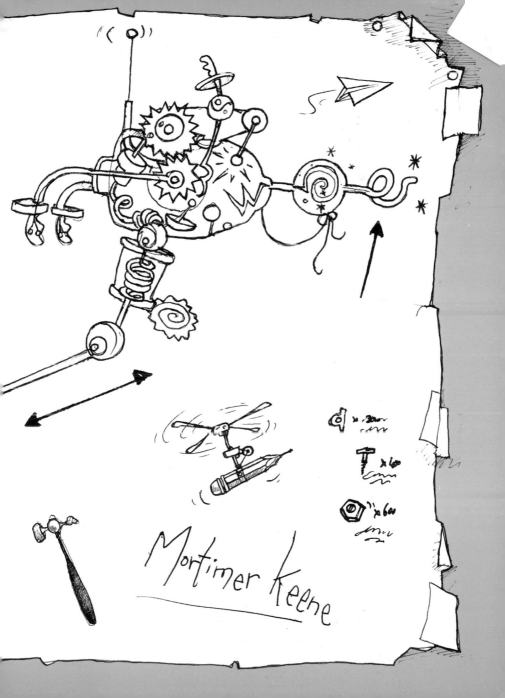

Mortimer Keene

Mortimer's
GRAVITY GUN!

Waste for recycling, including oranges to give colour to energy field

Super-grip handles

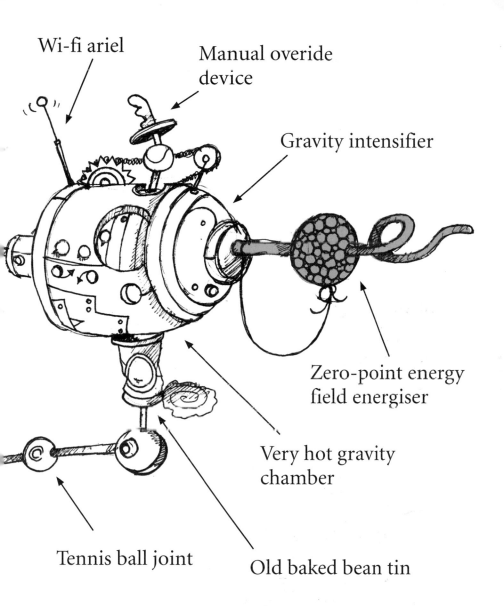

Wi-fi ariel

Manual overide device

Gravity intensifier

Zero-point energy field energiser

Very hot gravity chamber

Tennis ball joint

Old baked bean tin

A-Z OF ALIENS

ANDROMEDANS – aliens said to come from the Andromeda star system

BLACK TRIANGLES – huge, triangular UFOs, outlined by lights, which cruise silently over cities

CLOSE ENCOUNTERS – direct sightings of aliens (not just of their spacecraft)

DiSCS – mysterious flying discs have been reported throughout history

EXtRateRRestRial – a being from Space, not from Earth; an alien

FLYinG SauCeR – modern term for flying disc, widely used since 1947

GREMLINS – mysterious little beings believed to cause mischief in aircraft

HUMANOID – a creature that looks vaguely human but (gulp!) isn't

INTERGALACTIC TRAVEL – travel between galaxies (large star systems)

JET CHASES – military jets have sometimes been used to chase UFOs

KEENE, MORTIMER – leading expert on UFOs and extraterrestrials

LITTLE GREEN MEN – small humanoids with green skin and antennae on their heads. No, don't laugh…

MARTIANS – aliens said to come from the planet Mars

NOCTURNAL LIGHTS (NLS) – most UFO reports concern strange lights in the night sky

ORBS – some UFOs are ball-shaped, almost perfect spheres

PLEIADIANS – tall, fair-haired aliens said to come from the Pleiades star cluster

Quetzalcoatl – an ancient Aztec god who brought wisdom from the sky. Some say this was a very large UFO bringing extraterrestrial intelligence

Radar – use of radio waves to detect objects. UFOs have sometimes been picked up on radar screens

Secret Projects – are UFOs just new military aircraft that governments want to keep secret?

TRANSMISSIONS – radio messages from extraterrestrials

UFO – Unidentified Flying Object. Any mysterious object seen flying in the sky

VENUSIANS – aliens said to come from the planet Venus

WOBBLY – how sighting an alien can make you feel

X-Ray Machines – devices that can see through solid flesh. Used to examine strange creatures to see if the skeleton is human

Yikes! – common response to sighting an alien

Zetas – small, grey-skinned aliens, also known as 'Greys'

MORTiMeR'S UFO HUNTiNG Kit

1. Pen and notepad
Note down anything unusual seen in the sky, including weather conditions and the time of day. Draw sketch of the UFO.

2. Map of the local area
Note where you are viewing from.

3. Compass
In what direction is the UFO?

4. Camera
Can you get a photo of the UFO?

5. Binoculars
Has the UFO landed?
Take a closer look. Can
you see any aliens?

6. If so,
run like mad!

7. Don't be disappointed
if you see nothing at all.
Many UFO hunters spend
a lifetime searching
without results.

MORTIMER'S

Aliens come from different parts of the universe, but they all know this intergalactic language. It sounds like radio static, so pitch your voice high. Common questions are:

SNNSKNSNSKNSNS
What is your name?

VSSHHNSSHHtHNS
Where do you come from?

APHStHRROOPHRR
How are you?

GUIDE TO ALIEN SPEECH

PHLLPLNNLLLPHL
Do you speak English?

MMMMFtSYSKtS
Could you say that again?

RSSKtMRSSKtMR
Are you hungry?

XXYYYXNXX
Do you need the loo?

Common phrases:

KNSNMENSNS EMILY

My name is Emily.

HUBVSSHHNSS EARTH
I come from Earth.

MESSLERINKLPHRR
I'm feeling fine.

INVENT AN ALIEN!

Some people think there are no aliens. They are just invented by people with lively imaginations. How lively is your imagination? Can you invent an alien? Here are a few tips:

Where do they come from?
(What planet? Galaxy?)

What do their spacecraft look like?
(Flying disc? Rocket-shaped? Other?)

How tall are the aliens?

(10ft? 3ft? Other?)

What colour are they?

(Silver? Green? Pink with purple spots?)

Special features

(Are they humanoid? Monster-like? Machine-like? Do they have antennae?)

Now draw your alien, with a spacecraft, on a piece of paper.

978 0 340 99774 1

978 0 340 99773 4

MORTIMER KEENE

ALIEN
ABDUCTION

Tim Healey and
Chris Mould

978 0 340 99775 8

Look out for
these other
CRAZY
Mortimer
Books!